Anasazi Coloring Book

D1622044

Anasazi
Coloring Book

The Story of the *Ancestral Puebloans*

written and illustrated by

Sandra L. Stemmler

Today the Anasazi, the Ancient Ones,
are called Ancestral Puebloans.
Their descendants live along the
Rio Grande corridor in northern
New Mexico and into Arizona.

Native Voices

Book Publishing Company

Summertown, Tennessee

© 1997 Sandra L. Stemmler. All rights reserved

Cover design by Jeff Clark

Printed in the United States of America

Native Voices
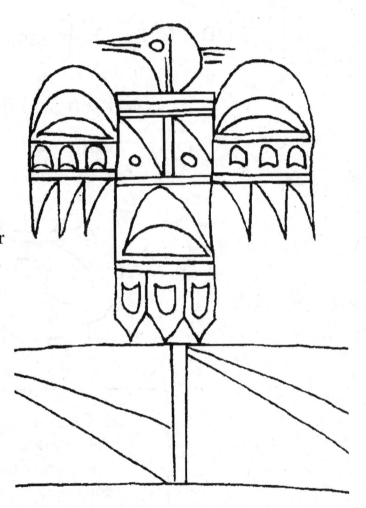
PO Box 99
Summertown, TN 38483
800-695-2241

ISBN 1-57067-042-0

ISBN13 978-1-57067-042-8

12 11 10 09 08 07   7 6 5 4 3 2

To My Readers:

This book has been created for your enjoyment. Blank pages have been left for you. Draw, take notes, or write your own story on them. Above all have fun with this little book that has been written especially for you.

The Book Publishing Co. is a member of Green Press Initiative. We have elected to print this title on paper with postconsumer recycled content and processed chlorine free, which saved the following natural resources:

BOOK
PUBLISHING
COMPANY

3 trees
135 lbs of solid waste
1,050 gallons of water
253 lbs of greenhouse gases
2 million BTUs

green
press
INITIATIVE

For more information visit: www.greenpressinitiative.org. Savings calculations thanks to the Environmental Defense Paper Calculator at www.papercalculator.org

The moon creeps silently along the rim of the mesa. It is searching for the children, for the people, for the Ancient Ones—the Anasazi.

They are gone.

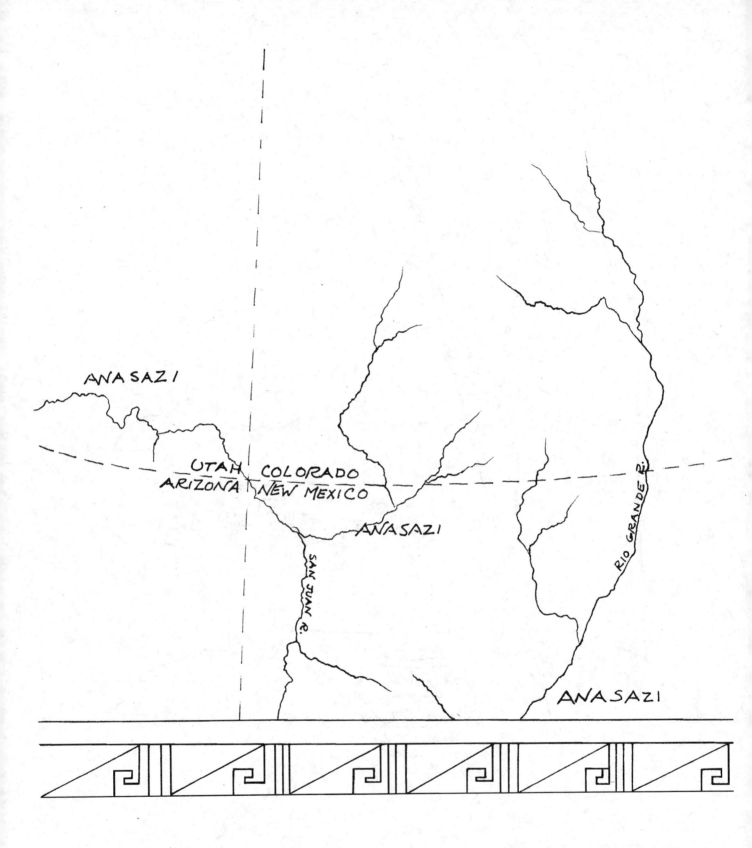

Many hundreds of years ago a group of American Indians lived in the southwest part of the United States.

They were called ANASAZI, or Ancient Ones.

In the beginning, the Anasazi were nomads who wandered the high plains in search of food. They lived in temporary shelters or caves.

The Anasazi hunted small game with spears, traps, nets, and snares. They also collected berries and plants for food and medicine.

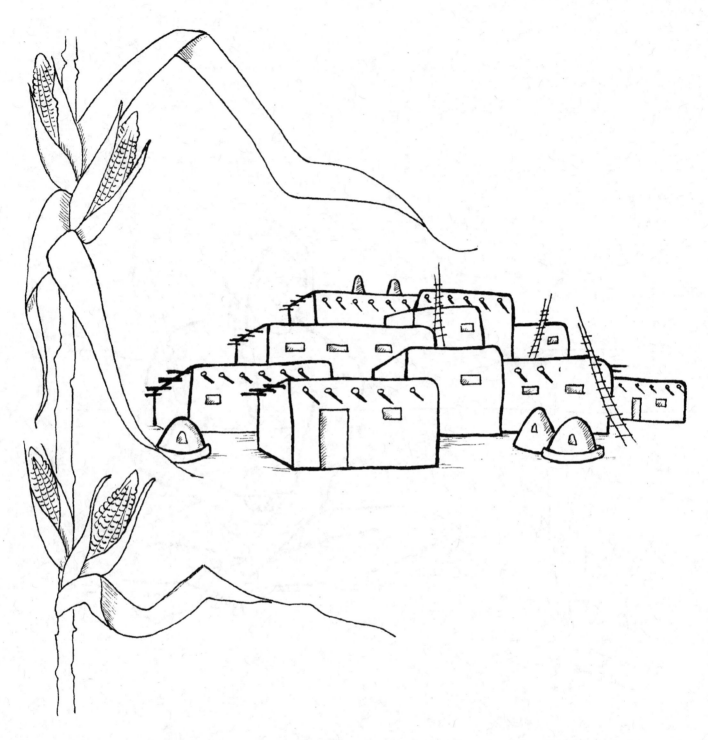

Corn was domesticated in 4000 BC. By 1000 BC, the Anasazi had learned to plant corn for the harvest. Because they had crops to tend, they stopped being nomads and built permanent houses. These houses were called PUEBLOS.

A pueblo is a group of houses built of poles and branches covered with ADOBE, which is straw or grass mixed with mud.

The Anasazi also built stone houses into the sides of cliffs. These buildings were called CLIFF DWELLINGS. They were constructed of overlapping layers of stone and plastered with mud. They were very durable. These cliff dwellings can still be visited today.

An Anasazi house had several rooms. It had a main room, with a fire pit, where the family would eat and sleep. The house also had several smaller rooms for storing food and tools. All the rooms were very small.

The Anasazi did not live like we do today. Their houses were only used for cooking and sleeping. The main part of their life was lived outside with other people of the village.

The people of the village would grind corn, make pottery, or work on their tools outside. Sometimes, they would work under RAMADAS. A ramada is like a house without walls. It was used for shade.

Always the people were together.

The Anasazi lived in harmony with the earth.

They had many CEREMONIES to celebrate the events of life. A ceremony is a time of singing, dancing, and prayer. The people had ceremonies for the crops and for the hunt.

Sometimes these ceremonies were held in special, separate rooms called KIVAS.

A kiva is a round room that is built under the ground. Entrance to the kiva is gained by a ladder in the roof. Special ceremonies, that included dancing, were held in the kivas. Sometimes the dancing went on all night.

High benches were built along the inside walls of the kiva. These benches were used as seats for people who were not dancing in the ceremony.

Kivas are still used today by pueblo people.

In the early morning, as the sun crept over the horizon, dancers left the kivas to lead the people in celebration.

There were dances to celebrate the seasons, to bless the corn and bean crops, to pray for meat from the hunt, and ask for plentiful water for the crops.

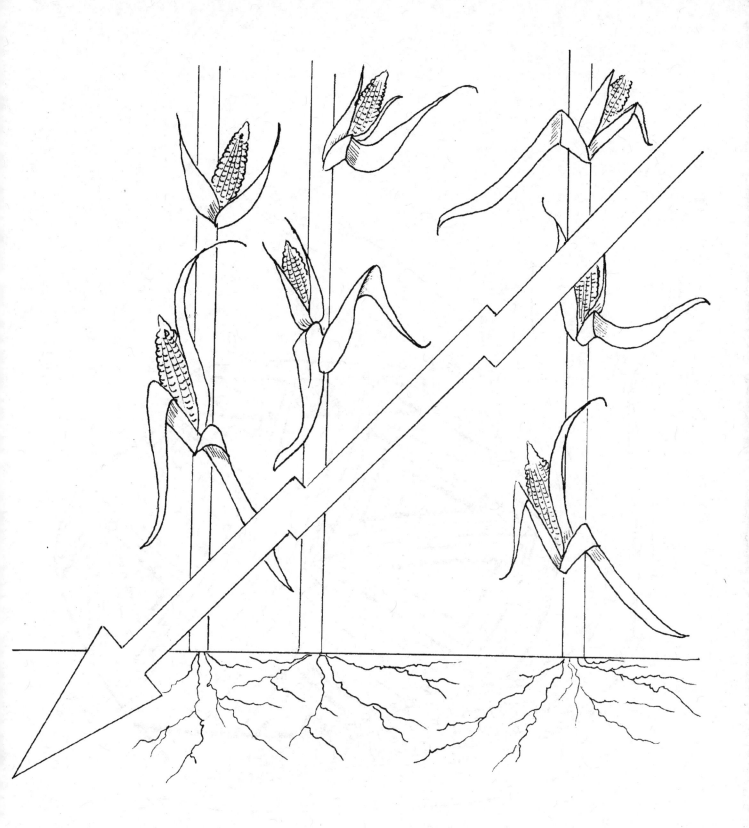

The greatest need the Anasazi had was for water. They lived in a high desert area where water was scarce. Many of their drawings or symbols tell about water. Symbols of rain and lightning are seen often because they mean life for the crops.

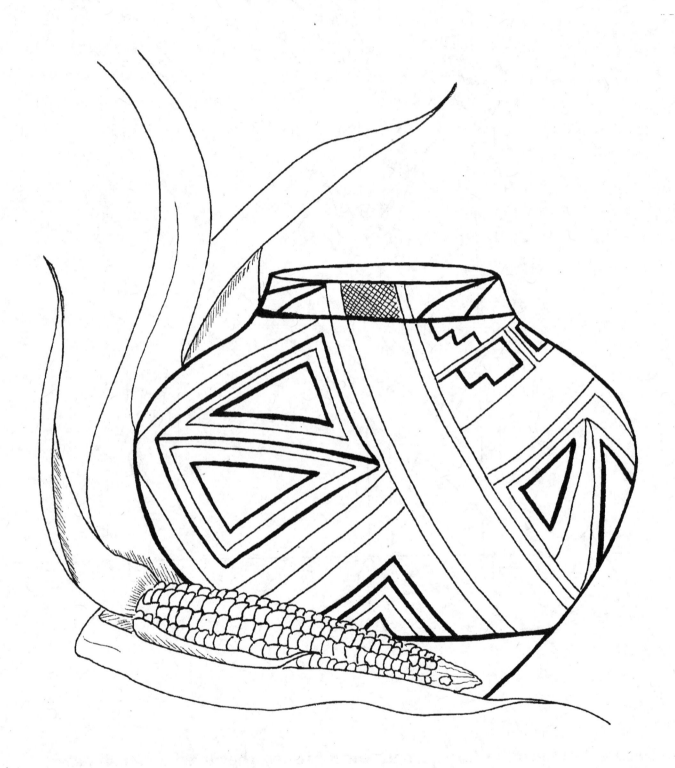

When the crops were gathered at the end of the summer season they were stored in the small rooms of the pueblos. Corn was removed from the cob and stored in pottery jars or woven baskets.

Pottery was made in the coil method. The bottom of the pot was placed on a woven pad. Coils of clay were wound up to the top of the jar. A piece of stone or wood was use to shape the jar.

Designs were painted on the pots. When they were dry, the pots were fired (baked) in a covered pit.

Much time was spent in food preparation. Corn was ground on a METATE or flat stone. The corn was pushed back and forth along the stone until it was ground into a flour-like substance that could be used for baking.

The Anasazi also ate seeds and nuts. These were hard to find as they were also a food source for animals and birds.

Food was gathered and brought back to the pueblo in a BURDEN BASKET, a large basket carried by a strap across the forehead.

The Anasazi use spears to kill wild game such as deer.

Fine spear heads were chipped from hard stones found in the area.

In the evening, perhaps the men of the village sat around the fire. Perhaps, they told stories to the children.

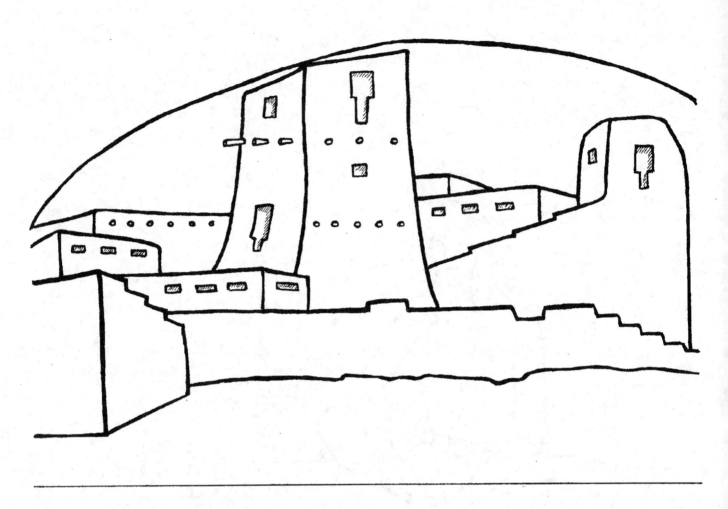

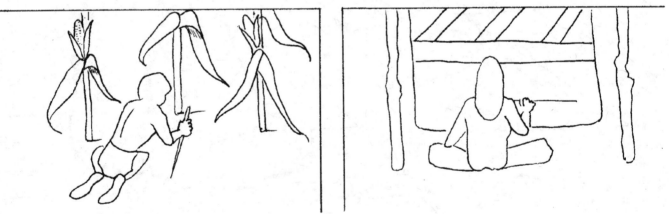

During the day, life in the village was busy and productive. The people built permanent dwellings in the pueblo style, or built massive cliff dwellings under the rims of the mesas. They tilled the soil and planted crops for the harvest. They hunted wild game to supplement their vegetable crops. They wove garments and made pottery.

Always they were together.

By 1000 AD, the Anasazi were comfortably settled into their life-style.

Two hundred and fifty years later they were gone. Were did they go? What happened to them?

There are several theories that try to answer these questions. One theory is that Navajo and Apache tribes drove them from their lands.

Some people think a long, dry spell forced them to abandon their fields for there was no water. Other people believe the Anasazi might have over-used the land by cutting too many trees and planting too many crops.

Most people believe they simply migrated to other areas.

Perhaps all these theories are true; perhaps none of them are true. Perhaps the Anasazi simply answered the moon and walked up the moonbeams to the stars.

VOCABULARY

ADOBE: a mud and straw mixture that is used to plaster the walls of buildings. It can also be formed into bricks to build houses.

ANASAZI, or ANCIENT ONES: a group of Southwest American Indians who lived in the Colorado, New Mexico, Utah, and Arizona area. They left this area about 1250 AD.

BURDEN BASKET: a large, woven basket, carried by a strap across the forehead.

CEREMONY: a special time of singing, dancing, and prayer.

CLIFF DWELLINGS: houses built of overlapping layers of stone. These houses were built under the rim of mesas.

KIVA: a round room, built slightly below the ground, which was used for ceremonies.

MESA: a flat-topped hill with cliff-like sides.

METATE: a large, flat stone that was used for grinding corn.

PUEBLOS: houses built of poles and branches and covered with adobe.

RAMADA: a temporary structure without walls that is used for shade.

THEORY: a mental way of looking at a situation or problem; a guess.

BIBLIOGRAPHY

Bahti, Tom, Southwestern Indian Tribes (Las Vegas: KC Publications, 1975).

Barry, John W., American Indian Pottery (Florence, Alabama: Books Americana, 1984).

Bunzel, Ruth L., The Pueblo Potter: A Study of Creative Imagination In Primitive Art (New York: Dover Publications, Inc., 1972).

Fewkes, Jesse Walter, Prehistoric Hopi Pottery Designs (New York: Dover Publications, Inc., 1973).

Highwater, Jamake, Ritual Of The Wind (Toronto: Methuen Publications, 1984).

Jones, DeWitt and Linda Cordell, Anasazi World (Portland: Graphic Arts Center Publishing Company, 1985).

Lister, Robert H. and Florence C., Those Who Came Before (Arizona: Southwest Parks and Monuments Association, 1983).

Stuart, David E., Glimpses of The Ancient Southwest (New Mexico: Ancient City Press, 1985).

Waters, Frank, Book Of The Hopi (United States of America: Penguin Books, 1984).

Wright, Barton, Hopi Kachinas (United States of America: Northland Publishing, 1988).

Activity and Coloring Books from Native Voices

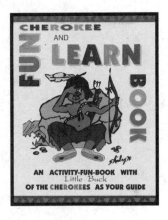

Cherokee Fun & Learn
J. Ed Sharpe
978-0-935741-03-2
$4.95

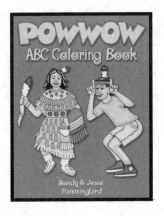

Powwow ABC
Sandy & Jessee Hummingbird
978-1-57067-096-1
$4.95

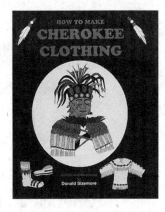

Cherokee Clothing
Sandy & Jessee Hummingbird
978-1-57067-180-7
$4.95

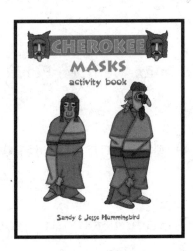

Cherokee Masks
Sandy & Jessee Hummingbird
978-1-57067-131-9

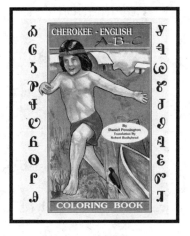

Cherokee ABC
Daniel Pennington
978-0-935741-18-6
$4.95

These books are available through your local bookstore or from:
Book Publishing Company
PO Box 99
Summertown, TN 38483
888-260-8458
Please include an additional $3.95 per book for shipping.

Activity and Coloring Books from Native Voices

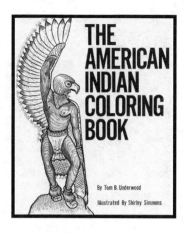

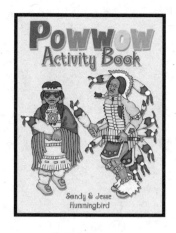

American Indian
Tom B. Underwood
978-0935741-02-5
$4.95

Powwow Activity
Sandy & Jessee Hummingbird
978-1-57067-078-7
$4.95

Yaqui
Stan Padilla
978-1-57067-068-8
$4.95

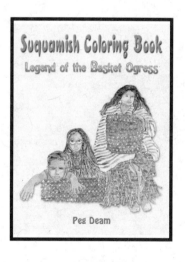

Native American Ledger Art
Sandy & Jessee Hummingbird
978-1-57067-119-7
$4.95

Suquamish
Peg Deam
978-1-57067-060-2
$4.95

These books are available through your local bookstore or from:
Book Publishing Company
PO Box 99
Summertown, TN 38483
888-260-8458
Please include an additional $3.95 per book for shipping.